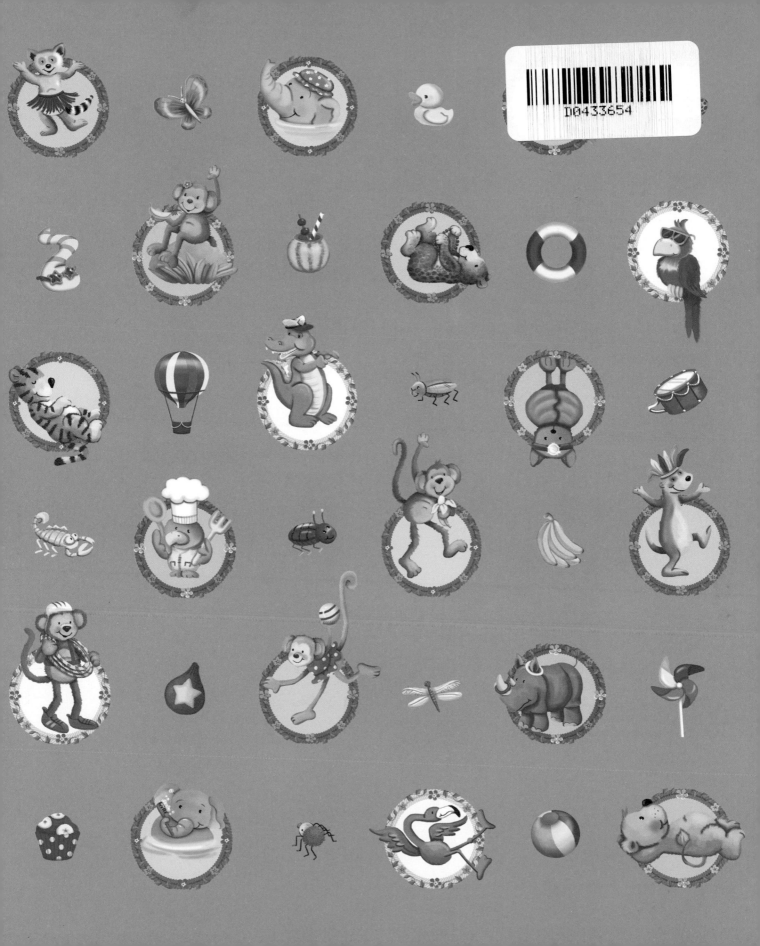

1001
Things to Find

1 parrot

3 snakes

2 elephants

4 lizards

5 flowers

Cheeky Monkey

igloobooks

Can you find 1001 cheeky monkey things?

Welcome to the tropical jungle, where Cheeky Monkey and his sister, Millie Monkey, are playing in their treetop tree house. They have found a special coconut with a golden star on it and inside is a scroll with a secret message.

"Find the 13 coconut clues, each with a secret scroll inside, to lead you to a jungle carnival celebration!" reads Cheeky Monkey.

Join Cheeky Monkey and Millie Monkey, as they search for the golden-star coconut clues. In each scene, you will need to find Cheeky Monkey, Millie Monkey and a coconut clue. There are over 1000 jungle items for you to find along the way, too, so let's get finding!

Cheeky Monkey

Coconut Clue

Millie Monkey

On the opposite page, see if you can spot Cheeky Monkey, Millie Monkey and the coconut clue. Once you've found them, see if you can spot the items below, too.

2 jungle lamps

8 bunches of grapes

11 blue crayons

Sunrise Safari

The cheeky monkeys are on an early morning safari in the savannah. Can you spot them among all their animal friends? Don't forget to look for the coconut clue!

1 bus driver

4 meerkats wearing jackets

5 sleeping cubs

6 suitcases

7 acacia trees

8 binoculars

9 pink bushes

10 map scrolls

11 camping lamps

13 red ants

Rainbow Falls

The monkeys reach the waterfall where the animals have their morning wash. Find them, as the elephants SPLISH and SPLASH! Can you see the next coconut clue?

5 elephants in shower caps

6 spotty umbrellas

8 rubber ducks

12 pink towels

15 bars of soap

Hidden Gems

Shhhh! It's time to explore a deep, dark cave. The walls are sparkling with jewels, but can you spot Cheeky Monkey and Millie? Where is the coconut clue hidden?

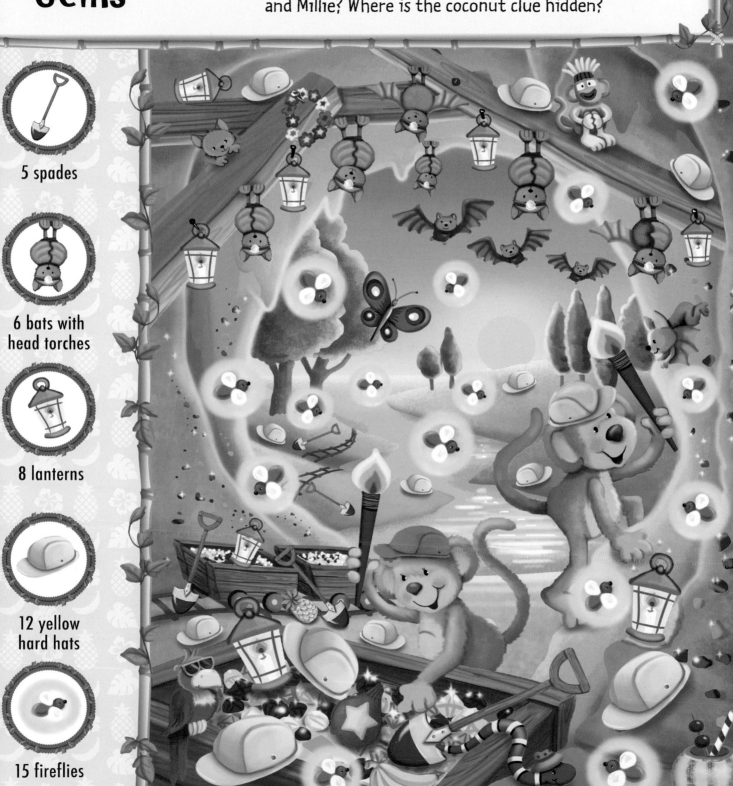

5 spades

6 bats with head torches

8 lanterns

12 yellow hard hats

15 fireflies

Paradise Island

Surf's up! Cheeky Monkey and Millie are ready for a cool drink. Can you see them on this secret island, perfect for a jungle getaway? Remember to find their next coconut clue.

1 totem pole

4 hula lemurs

5 surfboards

6 toucans

7 tribal masks

8 tiki torches

9 orange juice drinks

10 red flower garlands

11 stripy fish

13 purple shells

Rowing Rhinos

The cheeky monkeys arrive at the waterhole where the rhinos love to row in the sunshine. Can you spot them having fun on the boating lake? Where is the next clue?

5 red boats

6 spotty balls

8 baby rhinos in stripy swimsuits

12 bottles of suncream

15 toy boats

Up, Up and Away!

There's a cool breeze on the grassy plains, so it's the perfect time to fly a kite. Find Cheeky Monkey and Millie, as the tigers play. Remember to spot the next coconut clue.

5 hot-air balloons

6 toy windmills

8 kites

12 mice

15 pink butterflies

Swamp Cruise

Watch out, there are crocodiles about! Where are the monkeys on this spooky boat ride down the eerie swamp? Can you help them find their next coconut clue?

1 croc captain

4 life rings

5 pirate hats

6 blue flags

7 pirate fish

8 dragonflies

9 water barrels

10 oars

11 bush reeds

13 slimy rocks

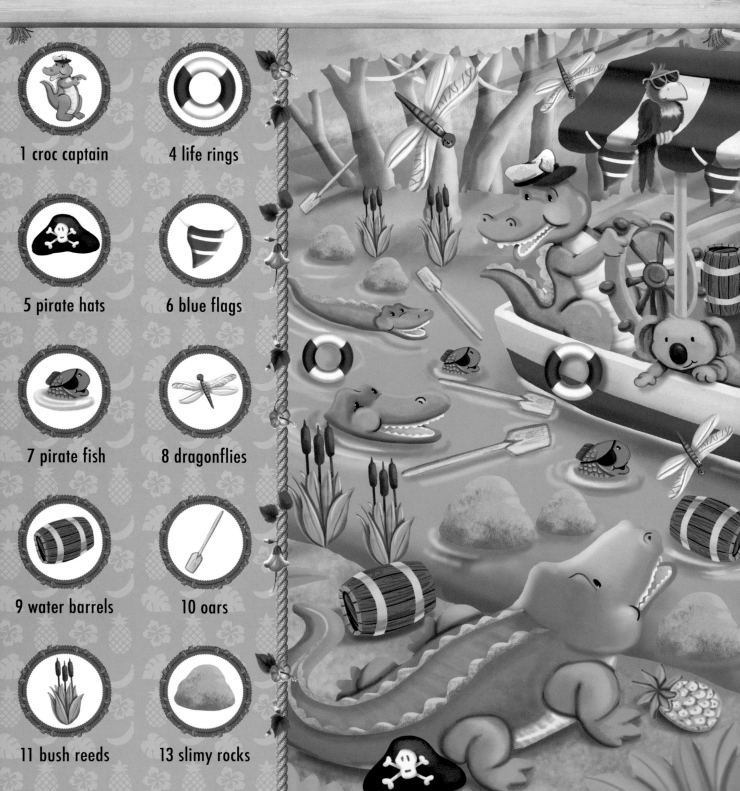

Jungle Gymnastics

Woo-hoo! Find Cheeky Monkey and Millie, as their other monkey friends perform their treetop tricks. Then, try and spot the coconut clue among the vines and leaves.

5 stripy hoops

6 top hats

8 bow ties

12 purple spiders

15 star fruit

Treetop Café

There's time for a quick bite, but there's still a clue to find among the Treetop Café customers. Can you see it?
See if you can spot the monkeys enjoying a tasty treat.

5 chef hats

6 menus

8 spotty plates

12 bamboo mugs

15 banana muffins

Lazy Lagoon

It's so relaxing in the quiet lagoon, but Cheeky Monkey is having so much fun. SPLASH! Can you spot him and Millie among the hippos and flamingos? Where is the clue?

1 hippo lifeguard

4 pink lilos

5 flamingos with goggles

6 rubber rings

7 beach balls

8 yellow fish

9 spotty flowers

10 lily pads

11 pink feathers

13 floating bubbles

Cheeky Explorers

There are bugs and insects galore on the jungle floor, but where are Cheeky Monkey and Millie? Help them find their next clue and get them one step closer to the carnival.

5 spotty frogs

6 yellow mangoes

8 purple worms

12 grasshoppers

15 red beetles

Rocky Climbers

The monkeys reach a tall, rocky cliff. Can you spot them and their coconut clue, as they prepare to climb all the way to the top? They'll need all their best equipment!

5 backpacks

6 purple climbing hooks

8 scorpions

12 water bottles

15 buzzing flies

Ancient Ruins

Cheeky Monkey and Millie search the jungle temple, while the leopards purr and prowl. Can you spot the clue before they do, among the treasure chests and statues?

1 stone statue

4 clay pots

5 treasure chests

6 giant ferns

7 pearl necklaces

8 piles of rubble

9 ruby rings

10 gold bricks

11 spotty lizards

13 red spiders

Carnival Celebration

It's party time! They've found all the coconut clues, so spot the cheeky monkeys dancing with all their friends at the carnival all night. Can you find the party items below, too?

1 DJ zebra

4 meerkats in headdresses

5 pink drums

6 feather boas

7 snakes in sparkly sunglasses

8 carnival flags

9 party hats

10 red balloons

11 party horns

13 streamers

Congratulations! You helped Cheeky Monkey and Millie Monkey make it all the way to the jungle carnival. Can you find each of these items in every jungle scene, too?

A monkey in a tribal mask

A giant spotty butterfly

A multicoloured garland

A golden pineapple

A drink in a melon cup

A snake in a safari hat

A parrot wearing sunglasses

A bunch of bananas

Were you looking closely? Go back and see if you can spot which scene each of these characters is hiding in.

A rhino holding hoops

A leaping dolphin

A sleeping leopard

An owl wearing a pirate hat